This book
belongs to:

Detective _____

Code name _____

Age _____

THE TRUTH ABOUT ZOOS

ANNIE'S AWESOME ADVENTURES

CELEBRATING 50 YEARS
the ZOO
LOUISVILLE
1969 – 2019
AT THE LOUISVILLE ZOO

WRITTEN BY KIM ALLGEIER

ILLUSTRATED BY J. L. R. HARRINGTON

ISBN: 978-1-941953-89-1

Library of Congress Control Number: 2020902247

Written by Kim Allgeier
Edited by Kelly Grether and Kim Allgeier

Illustrated by J. L. R. Harrington
Designed by J. L. R. Harrington and Scott Stortz

Published and distributed by Butler Books, Louisville, Kentucky
www.butlerbooks.com, info@butlerbooks.com

Printed in Canada

The Louisville Zoo, a nonprofit organization and state zoo of Kentucky, is dedicated to bettering the bond between people and our planet by providing excellent care for animals, a great experience for visitors, and leadership in scientific research and conservation education.

The Louisville Zoo is one of 238 organizations accredited by the Association of Zoos and Aquariums (AZA). To learn more about AZA and its world-class zoo and aquarium members and programs, visit www.AZA.org.

To learn more about the Louisville Zoo, purchase a membership, volunteer, or donate to the Zoo, visit www.LouisvilleZoo.org.

ACKNOWLEDGMENTS

The Louisville Zoo wishes to thank its dedicated, passionate, and caring staff members over the past 50 years. It certainly takes a village to operate a zoo! Every department and person has played a key role in making the Zoo successful. You showed up, inspired, educated, loved, lost, and made every single day count.

Special thanks to the Humana Foundation, Annette Cox, and Jessica and Mac Thompson for their support of this book. You encouraged the Zoo to find a bold, new way to share its story, and we believe this book accomplishes that. Your energy, passion for animals, and appreciation of the Zoo's role within the community, region, and world is greatly valued and inspiring to so many. Thank you!

The Zoo also wishes to recognize its 50th Celebration presenting sponsor, Whittenberg Construction. Thank you for your support and hard work on so many projects over the years.

Many thanks to everyone who has visited, volunteered, advocated, cared for an animal, attended an event, bought a membership, and donated to the Louisville Zoo over the past 50 years. Your support of the Zoo, animals, and staff has been nothing short of amazing.

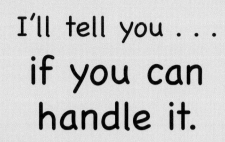

ANNIE'S ELABORATE PLAN TO BREAK THIS CASE WIDE OPEN!

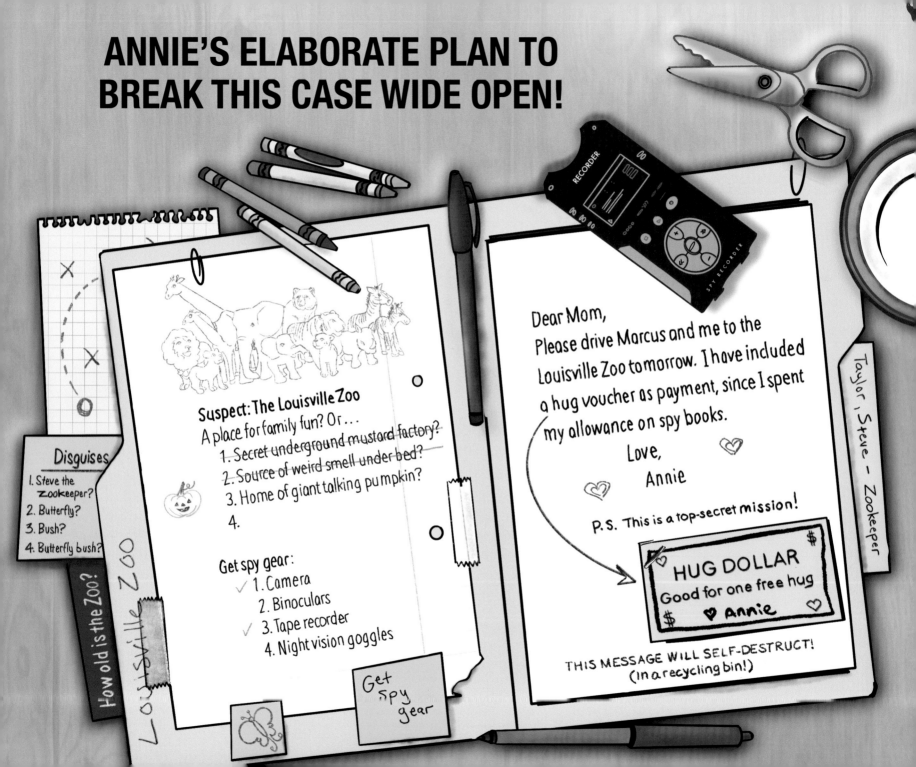

Suspect: The Louisville Zoo
A place for family fun? Or...
1. Secret underground mustard factory?
2. Source of weird smell under bed?
3. Home of giant talking pumpkin?
4.

Get spy gear:
✓ 1. Camera
  2. Binoculars
✓ 3. Tape recorder
  4. Night vision goggles

Disguises
1. Steve the Zookeeper?
2. Butterfly?
3. Bush?
4. Butterfly bush?

How old is the Zoo?

Louisville Zoo

Get spy gear

Taylor, Steve - Zookeeper

Dear Mom,
Please drive Marcus and me to the Louisville Zoo tomorrow. I have included a hug voucher as payment, since I spent my allowance on spy books.
    Love,
    Annie

P.S. This is a top-secret mission!

HUG DOLLAR
Good for one free hug
♡ Annie

THIS MESSAGE WILL SELF-DESTRUCT!
(In a recycling bin!)

RECORDER

SPY RECORDER

It's for the animals. They live here and need around-the-clock care. Any time they have a problem, the zoo vets help them. They **DO** give checkups . . . **JUST NOT TO KIDS.**

WHAT'S THE TRUTH ABOUT ZOOS?

Annie and Marcus used their detective skills to learn some pretty amazing things about the Louisville Zoo. Here are some things you might have missed or want to know more about.

STEVE TAYLOR

In Annie's elaborate plan, she dresses herself as a familiar friendly face at the Louisville Zoo—the Zoo's very own Steve Taylor. Steve started his career as a vet tech in 1975 and has seen the Zoo grow by leaps and bounds. He has served as the Zoo's assistant director of conservation, education, and collections since 2014. His favorite animal is the grey seal. He can often be found walking the Zoo to observe animals and assist keepers. One of his favorite places to visit is the Zoo's Gorilla Forest sanctuary.

GIANT TALKING PUMPKIN

Say cheese! Annie's plan also mentions another familiar face, Mumpkin the Pumpkin. Mumpkin has been smiling in Louisville family photos snapped during the Zoo's "World's Largest Halloween Party" for more than 20 years. She loves to talk with kids about Halloween, costumes, and candy.

50TH ANNIVERSARY CELEBRATION

From 1969 to 2019—the math does add up! The Louisville Zoo officially opened full-time on May 1, 1969. It celebrated its 50th anniversary in 2019 with a public celebration at the Zoo, outreach events in the community, a special 50th anniversary poster, the opening of Colobus Crossing and Snow Leopard Pass, the birth of a male African elephant calf, a history book, and this children's book.

Over the past 50 years, more than 28 million people have visited the Louisville Zoo, which is the area's #1 nonprofit attraction.

GROSS SMELL, SWEET MYSTERY

That gross smell is not much of a mystery! Caring for animals is a big job and that includes cleaning up after them. After all, what goes in, must come out, right? If you come to the Zoo early, you might spot staff driving the Zoo Poopy-Doo truck around to collect the animals' waste so it can be turned into compost for the spring. Would you like to help your garden grow? The Zoo sells Zoo Poopy-Doo compost every April.

ZOO VETS

The Zoo's Animal Health Center team is integral to the overall welfare of its animals. Yes, it's true, the animals do get biannual checkups, which include an eye exam, dental exam, bloodwork, and a physical. These exams, along with routine visits and emergency care, are overseen by a team of two veterinarians, three vet techs, and one zookeeper. Human specialists, like pediatricians, cardiologists, and ophthalmologists, also provide assistance for some procedures. Just like us, sometimes a home health care visit is what is best for a patient. The animal health team uses a bike and small trailer to carry medication and supplies from the Zoo's hospital to an animal's exhibit area for treatment.

ZOOKEEPERS

Zookeepers do it all! They provide daily checkups for animals that occur during regular animal presentations for Zoo guests and behind the scenes in their bedrooms and dens. They clean animal areas, prepare food, talk with visitors about conservation efforts, and so much more. The Zoo's dedicated team of keepers collectively have over 840 years of experience caring for wild animals. Many of them started at the Zoo as volunteers when they were just 13 years old.

JOHN WALCZAK

Marcus and Annie learn about animal rotation from another friendly face—Zoo Director John Walczak. John was hired to be the curator of the HerpAquarium in 1985. In 1996, as assistant director of the Zoo, he helped open the Islands exhibit—home to animals such as the orangutans, siamangs, Sumatran tigers, babirusa pigs, and Malayan tapirs. He has also brought Glacier Run, Lorikeet Landing, Snow Leopard Pass, Colobus Crossing, the Conservation Carousel, and so many other wonderful things to the Zoo. John has served as director since 2004. If you catch him walking around the Zoo, ask him what his favorite animal is. (Hint: There are currently 7.6 billion of them on the planet and they have the power to save species and nature.)

BE THE DETECTIVE

Along their adventure, Annie and Marcus discovered evidence of the Zoo's animal care plans. On your next outing to the Zoo, what can you find?

SIGNS OF ENRICHMENT

You may be wondering what that weird ball of hay is hanging in the elephant yard. It's an enrichment item. Interactions like allowing animals to hunt for hidden treats, to experience new smells, to use passages, or to have a new item to play with enriches their lives at the Zoo; keeps them active, thinking, and learning; and encourages their natural exploratory and foraging behaviors.

 Look around the Zoo: Can you spot enrichment items like cardboard tubes, balls, or paper bags filled with hidden treats?

 Look around your house: What do you see that you could do with your pets at home?

ANIMAL DIETS
Blueberries, apples, and bananas . . . oh my!

The Zoo has a kitchen for the animals called the commissary. It's the "engine" of the Zoo, where excellent care for the animals begins. Most of the food for the animals is stored, prepared, and measured in this space. Fruit, vegetables, insects, mice, and dry food products are kept here. Some animals, like gorillas, bears, seals, and sea lions, eat so much food their supplies are stored in refrigerators and freezers at their exhibits.

Do you know which animals at the Zoo eat the most food in a day? The gorillas!

 Look around the Zoo: Can you find the animals' food in their habitats? (Hint: An animal's diet may not look like the food we eat.)

 Look around your house: How can you change your pet's diet to include special foods or treats?

ANIMAL ROTATION AND TRAINING

How do animals such as the orangutans, Sumatran tigers, and Malayan tapirs move from their bedrooms to various locations within their outdoor habitats?

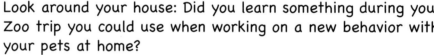

The Zoo's Islands exhibit was the first in the world to use multi-species animal rotation, which means the mammals at Islands rotate in and out of varied habitat spaces at unpredictable times. But why?

The natural world offers variety . . . naturally. Animal rotation gives the Zoo's animals variety, mimicking what they would experience in nature, keeping them active and curious. Like Islands, many of the Zoo's exhibits, such as Gorilla Forest, Snow Leopard Pass, and Glacier Run, use rotation.

Training is key to a successful relationship between keepers and animals. It allows the Zoo's expert staff the chance to build a relationship of trust with an animal, observe behavior, give routine care checkups, and administer medicine with the animal's full cooperation.

Look around the Zoo: During your next visit to the Zoo, try to find time to watch an animal presentation or talk to a keeper. When you return home, draw pictures of the animal care you were able to see or something you learned from a keeper.

Look around your house: Did you learn something during your Zoo trip you could use when working on a new behavior with your pets at home?

ABOUT THE AUTHOR

Kim Allgeier has been the curator of conservation education for the Louisville Zoo since 2014. She has more than 15 years of experience working for museums, parks, libraries, and zoos, providing educational opportunities for children. Kim is a passionate educator who believes in the power of connecting kids through experiences in our community and providing access for all children to discover, explore, and expand their worldview. She is a graduate of Western Kentucky University and lives in Louisville with her husband, Philip, and her daughter, Audrey, and is expecting her second child this spring. This is her first children's book.

ABOUT THE ILLUSTRATOR

J. L. R. Harrington, a longtime Louisville resident, is CEO of Design Web and a classically trained oil painter from the Maryland Institute of Art. She is an enthusiastic supporter of fairness, accessibility, and promotion of technology in arts education through several local and national arts-awareness programs. Harrington draws all of her inspiration from her business partner/ husband and her three pun-tolerant sons. Her favorite Louisville Zoo animals are the aquatic species and box turtles.

50TH CELEBRATION CONTRIBUTORS

AT&T
Gail Becker
Central Bank
Wendy Dant Chesser
Comfy Cow
Natalie and Condrad Daniels
Mr. and Mrs. David Daulton
Sandra A. Frazier
Frazier-Joy Family Foundation
Genentech
Heidi Hulon, DVM
Humana Foundation
Mrs. Deborah C. King
Estate of Anna Kruer

Louisville Metro Council
Louisville Tourism
Neil and Jane MacDonald
MPI Printing
Moon Leasing, Inc.
Brad and Becky Phillips
Pizzazzle Events
The John Schnatter Family Foundation
Spear Corporation
William E. Summers IV
White Clay
Jan West and Jonathan Goldberg
Whittenberg Construction
WordsFresh

Special Thanks To

Annette Cox
Marcelle Gianelloni
Debbie Sebree
Sam Stewart
Jessica Thompson